Introduction

Welcome to Mega Flash!

Mega Flash is the new and improved version of everyone's favorite Primary Grammar series, Flash.

This series was developed to make grammar more fun and interesting. A wide variety of activities and exercises throughout the book make complex grammatical structures more understandable and accessible.

The reading, writing and new listening exercises included in the series help you to:
- write sentences using pronouns, adjectives, adverbs and prepositions
- use plurals, contractions and negatives
- learn about regular and irregular verbs and their use in different tenses
- write questions and answers
- organize and structure main ideas and detailed sentences
- summarize, categorize and classify information
- develop fluency and accuracy in all aspects of English

Mega Flash provides everything you need to know about the basics of the English language and helps to make grammar come alive!

Contents

This is my book!

Name: _____

School: _____

Class: _____

Use a capital letter for the first word in a sentence:

Mary has a new bicycle.

in the greeting and closing of a letter:

Dear Sir, Dear Susan, Yours sincerely,

and for the first word of a direct quotation:

Jim asked, "**Do** you want to go to the movies?"

Also use a capital letter for the names of people and pet animals:

Richard, Sylvia, Butch, Trixy

the names of geographical features like oceans, seas, rivers, mountains:

Atlantic Ocean, Red Sea, River Thames, Alps

the names of clubs, companies, organizations, institutions:

Boy Scouts, Red Cross, Department of Energy

the names of months, days, special occasions, and holidays:

October, Tuesday, Christmas, Halloween

the names of airlines and trains and the makes of cars and other vehicles:

Delta Airlines, Aeromexico, Orient Express, Chrysler

the names of continents, countries, states, cities, towns, streets, buildings:

Africa, Brazil, Arizona, Athens, West Road, City Hall

the names of nationalities and languages:

Mexican, Italian, Japanese, English, Turkish, French

and the main words in the titles of T.V. programs, movies, books, magazines, and poems:

Saved by the **Bell, Men** in **Black, Mega Flash, Premier, Hiawatha**

1

Rewrite each sentence using capital letters where needed.

Example: The third sunday in june is father's day.
The third Sunday in June is Father's Day.

1. the rio grande river crosses both mexico and the united states.

2. many spanish-speaking people live in los angeles, california.

3. christmas day is celebrated on december 25th.

4. i read a wonderful book called the wizard of oz last august.

5. i have many french, english, and spanish-speaking friends.

6. all the children love to watch sesame street on saturday mornings.

7. jane is my best friend and she went with me to disneyland last april.

8. we are going to acapulco, mexico on our easter vacation.

9. i have swimming classes on mondays and wednesdays.

10. of all the seasons i like autumn most of all.

Use a period at the end of statements and normal commands:

> They went home.   It's snowing.   Be quiet, please.

after an initial in a name:

> John F. Kennedy

and after many abbreviations:

> Dr.   St.   m.p.h.

Use a question mark at the end of any question:

> Did you buy some milk?   Are you feeling okay?
> Where am I?   What are you doing?

Use an exclamation point after an exclamation or command that shows strong feelings:

> It's disgusting!   Come quickly!   What a great party!
> Stop that!   Surprise!   Ouch! That hurts!

Correct each sentence with periods, question marks, and exclamation points where necessary.

1. Hurry up and finish that right now

2. Can he get dressed on his own

3. They live on Eldridge Ave near the Harry S Truman Library

4. Her appointment with Dr Willis is at four o'clock

5. Stop it

6. Will you take a train to San Antonio

Use an apostrophe to show where letters have been left out in contractions:

    can't   we're   I'd   won't

and to show ownership:

    Maria's sweater   the teacher's book

Use a comma to separate words or phrases in a list:

    We have our swimming lessons on Tuesdays, Thursdays, and Saturdays.

    She bought pencils, notebooks, erasers, and a pen.

before the connector in a compound sentence:

    I wanted to taste the grapes, but they were sour.

after Yes and No in short answers to yes/no questions:

    Yes, I'll go.   No, I can't go.

to separate clauses within a sentence:

    The baby looks chubby, even though he doesn't eat much.

to separate a state and a country or a town and a state:

    I like to go to San Antonio, Texas.

to separate numbers (every 3 digits):

    $22,778   4,560

and after the greeting and closing of a letter:

    Dear Mr. Lewis, Dear Sir, Love, Yours sincerely,

Rewrite each sentence using capital letters, commas, periods, question marks, exclamation points, and apostrophes wherever needed.

Example: mr dell works at jc penny in the mens dept

Mr. Dell works at J.C. Penny in the men's dept.

1. what are you doing during christmas dr smith

2. i read the book moby dick twice

3. dont jump there

4. dr green will see you now mr johnson

5. happy birthday surprise

6. did carla go to disneyland last october

7. i wanted to go to the movies but i didnt have any money

8. she bought apples tomatoes and bananas on thursday

9. dr brown works at the general hospital

10. yes i can go see the movie scream with you on saturday

11. this car has traveled 32842 km in one week

12. wow she speaks english italian and french

Listen to the words and circle their abbreviations. Then copy them.

Days of the Week

Sunday	Sun.
Monday	Mon.
Tuesday	Tues.
Wednesday	Wed.
Thursday	Thur.
Friday	Fri.
Saturday	Sat.

Months of the Year

January	Jan.
February	Feb.
March	Mar.
April	Apr.
August	Aug.
September	Sept.
October	Oct.
November	Nov.
December	Dec.

Titles

Mister	Mr.
Junior	Jr.
Senior	Sr.
Doctor	Dr.
General	Gen.

Units of Measurement

inch	in.
foot	ft.
miles per hour	m.p.h.
ounce	oz.
pound	lb.
pint	pt.
quart	qt.
gallon	gal.
centimeter	cm.
meter	m.
kilometer	km.
gram	g.
kilogram	kg.
liter	L.

Mark Johnson Jr.
Gen. Dir. of the
Ark. Fruit Co.
Ltd.

States and Streets

California	Cal.
Florida	Flo.
Arkansas	Ark.
Arizona	Arz.
Texas	Tex.
Road	Rd.
Street	St.
Drive	Dr.
Avenue	Ave.

Organizations

Department	Dept.
Company	Co.
Incorporated	Inc.
Limited	Ltd.
Institute	Inst.
Society	Soc.
Association	Assn.

A common noun is the general name of a person, place, or thing.
A common noun begins with a small letter:
    cat   stadium   city
A proper noun is the name of a particular person, place, or thing.
A proper noun begins with a capital letter:
    Susie
    San Francisco Stadium
    Mexico City

Write each noun in the correct planet.

Kennedy Airport   dentist
nightgown   American School
shelf   Dr. Smith
piano   Robert
clip   John
bulletin board   Halloween
Peter Pan   Mississippi

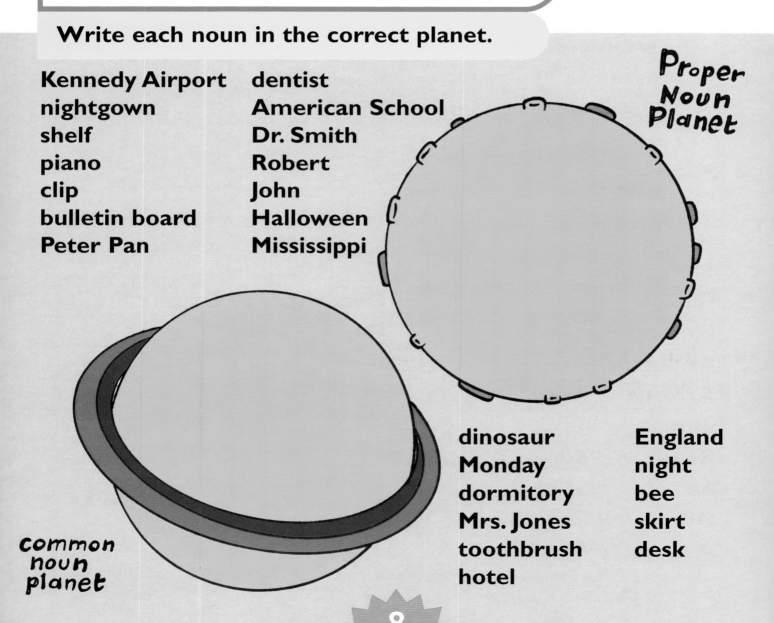

Proper Noun Planet

common noun planet

dinosaur   England
Monday   night
dormitory   bee
Mrs. Jones   skirt
toothbrush   desk
hotel

To form the plural of most regular nouns, add –s:

tack   tacks   clip   clips   girl   girls

With nouns that end in –s, –sh, –ch, or –x, add –es:

dress   dresses   dish   dishes

watch   watches   box   boxes

With nouns that end in a consonant and –y, change the y to i and add –es:

baby   babies   cherry   cherries   pony   ponies

With nouns that end in –f or –fe, change the –f to –v and add –s or –es:

wolf   wolves   knife   knives   leaf   leaves

With some nouns the singular and plural forms are the same:

deer   deer   fish   fish   sheep   sheep

tuna   tuna   salmon   salmon

With some nouns, the plural form is irregular:

goose   geese   tooth   teeth   mouse   mice

foot   feet   man   men   ox   oxen

woman   women   child   children

Write the plural form of each noun.

1. dish
2. ticket
3. lady
4. box
5. policeman
6. calf
7. witch
8. class

9. life
10. fly
11. peach
12. army
13. church
14. wolf
15. woman
16. salmon

Listen and repeat the plurals.

In each sentence, underline the correct form of the noun.

Example: Some of the calf/<u>calves</u> were eating in the field.

1. Yesterday we picked up all the leaves/leaf from the big oak tree.

2. The men ran away when a big fierce wolf/wolves appeared.

3. The hen walked proudly with all her little chick/chicks behind her.

4. Put all the new books on those shelf/shelves, please.

5. The monkeys ate four big bunch/bunches of bananas.

6. There is a very old church/churches in the village.

Listen and check your answers.

10

A very common way to show possession or ownership is the use of an apostrophe (') and –s.

With a singular noun, add an apostrophe and –s:

my brother's bike   the girl's bedroom

With a plural noun which ends in –s, simply add an apostrophe:

my friends' schoolbags   your parents' house

With a plural noun which does not end in –s, add an apostrophe and –s:

the men's hats   the children's games

Write phrases that show ownership.

Example: (parents)   (children)
        the children's parents

1. (tail) (dog) _____

2. (hats) (women) _____

3. (house) (friends) _____

4. (toys) (children) _____

5. (book) (student) _____

6. (wife) (uncle) _____

7. (jacket) (Robert) _____

8. (medicine) (patients) _____

We use a pronoun in place of a noun. Sometimes we use a pronoun to replace the subject of a sentence and sometimes to replace the object.

Subject pronouns	Object pronouns
singular:	singular:
I you he she it	me you him her it
plural:	plural:
we you they	us you them
Subject	**Object**
I sit next to Billy.	Alan sits in front of me.
Martha plays the guitar.	The policeman talks to the man.
She plays the guitar.	The policeman talks to him.
My cousins live in Sacramento.	I watch videos with my friends.
They live in Sacramento.	I watch videos with them.

After each sentence, write subject if the pronoun replaces the subject and object if the pronoun replaces the object.

Example: He and Carl went sailing.　　　**Subject**

1. Sally and I went shopping. _____

2. We went to the movies. _____

3. The teacher took us to the museum. _____

4. He gave the bicycle to the boys. _____

5. Please take these books to him. _____

6. Anna took Jenny and me to the party. _____

Underline the correct pronoun in each sentence.

Example: Alice and I/me went to the movies.

1. We/Us went to the football game.

2. The teacher took we/us to the library.

3. Him/He was a famous pilot.

4. Aunt Mary gave us/we $1.00.

5. Her/She and I are best friends.

6. Please take this workbook to he/him.

7. Charlie took Alan and me/I to the party.

8. The teacher told she/her to talk louder.

9. You and he/him gave a good report.

10. She/her and Karen went shopping.

11. I saw he/him in the park yesterday.

12. He sent her/she some flowers for her birthday.

Listen and check your answers.

Possessive pronouns show possession and always go after the noun.

> That book is mine.   Don't touch that. It's hers.
> Is this car yours?   These toys are theirs.

Remember, none of the possessive pronouns is written with an apostrophe.

Listen, read, and repeat the words.

Subject Pronouns		Possessive Pronouns	
I	it	mine	its
you	we	yours	ours
he	you	his	yours
she	they	hers	theirs

Complete each sentence with the correct possessive pronoun.

1. That dog is _____. (we)
2. Those flowers are _____. (she)
3. The baby bottle is _____. (he)
4. Those books are _____. (I)
5. These dresses are _____. (they)

Write five sentences using possessive pronouns.

1. _____
2. _____
3. _____
4. _____
5. _____

A **sentence** is a group of words that expresses a complete thought and contains a **subject** and a **predicate** which includes a **verb**:

> Jane forgot her homework.

The **subject** tells us who or what performs the action of the verb.

The subject can be one word or a group of words:

> Sandra drank some milk.
>
> Those noisy dogs wake me up every morning.

The **predicate** tells what the subject does, is, or has.

The predicate can also be one word or a group of words:

> All the children laughed.
>
> My father cooks breakfast on the weekend.

In each sentence, circle the subject and underline the predicate.

1. Mrs. Brown went to see Mary's teacher.

2. Monica's birthday is in July.

3. The policemen stopped the traffic.

4. My mother and grandmother are making cookies in the kitchen.

5. Our baseball team played hard all winter.

6. The teacher dictated the sentences slowly.

7. The football rolled into the street.

8. The angry man kicked the dog.

9. The architect built the new houses on this block.

10. The waiter and waitress scolded the children for being so messy.

Write a predicate for each of the following subjects.

Example: Mary played with her dolls in the bedroom.

1. Our teacher _____

2. The spacecraft _____

3. My uncle _____

4. The witch _____

5. Mr. Davis _____

6. Dr. Harrison _____

7. The flowers _____

8. The funny-looking Martians _____

Write a subject for each of the following predicates.

1. _____ was very noisy.

2. _____ were funny.

3. _____ fixed the car.

4. _____ ran into the barn.

5. _____ cried all night.

6. _____ was under the table.

7. _____ were mad and started shouting.

8. _____ put the toys in our stockings.

The **verb** of the sentence has to agree with the subject. For example, in the present simple tense, if the subject is the third person singular (he, she, or it), add –s:

    I sell pizza.   He sells pizza.

    They play chess.   She plays chess.

Spelling Rules

With verbs that end in –e, just add –s:

    bake – bakes   like – likes

With verbs that end in –o, –sh, –ch, –ss, –zz, or –x, add –es:

    go – goes   dress – dresses   finish – finishes

    buzz – buzzes   catch – catches   fix – fixes

With verbs that end in a consonant and –y, change the –y to –i and add –es:

try – tries   carry – carries

Complete the table with the correct forms of each verb.

1. I fly	it	
2. I fish	they	
3. I sweep	we	
4. I worry	she	
5. I kiss	he	
6. I go	you	
7. I mix	they	
8. I touch	she	

Listen and check your answers.

Complete each sentence with the correct form of the given verb.

Example: He works every day after school. (work)

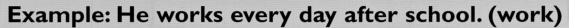

1. Martin _____ to dance with his girlfriend. (like)

2. My aunt _____ flowers in the garden every spring. (plant)

3. Astronomers _____ at the stars through a telescope. (look)

4. The janitor _____ the school every afternoon. (clean)

5. Mothers _____ at their babies. (smile)

6. The baby _____ when she is hungry. (cry)

7. The professor _____ the lesson carefully every day. (read)

8. The horses _____ over the fence. (jump)

9. My sisters _____ cookies with my aunt in the mornings. (bake)

10. Mr. Smith _____ his car on Saturdays. (fix)

Listen and check your answers.

A. Rewrite each sentence using capital letters, periods, commas, question marks, exclamation points, **and** apostrophes **where necessary.**

Example: we saw the movie titanic last saturday
We saw the movie Titanic last Saturday.

1. i was born on november 29th 1988 in paris france

_____

2. does the smith family live on jefferson street

_____

3. hurry up and finish that right now

_____

4. janes mother went to see dr rivers because she felt sick

_____

5. did you watch that program called tornado last night

_____

6. one of my favorite books is the jungle book

_____

7. carl and bob went to visit bobs sister at central hospital

_____

8. music class will be on mondays wednesdays and thursdays

_____

B. Write the plural form of each noun.

1. crash
2. table
3. baby
4. fox
5. policeman
6. scarf
7. stitch
8. glass

9. wife
10. pony
11. beach
12. cherry
13. watch
14. leaf
15. man
16. deer

C. In each sentence, underline the correct form of the noun.

Example: Some of the wolf/wolves came out of the forest.

1. Yesterday we drew many different leaves/leaf in our notebooks.

2. The farmer has just one cow and one calf/calves.

3. The duck swam on the pond with all her little duckling/ducklings behind her.

4. I need to put up some new shelf/shelves in my office.

5. He gave his mom a big bunch/bunches of flowers on Mother's Day.

6. The beach/beaches is very crowded during Easter vacation.

D. Rewrite each phrase to show possession.

1. the tails of the rabbits _____

2. the books of the teacher _____

3. the husband of the woman _____

4. the grades of the students _____

5. the teachers of my brother _____

E. Underline the correct pronoun in each sentence.

Example: We/Us had ice cream for dessert.

1. His mother took he/him to the dentist.

2. My grandma gave we/us some cookies.

3. I saw them/they at the shopping mall.

4. Please give this book to she/her.

5. Sally and I/me are really good friends.

F. Complete the table with the correct forms of each verb.

1. I _____	she cries
2. I wish	they _____
3. I worry	she _____
4. I _____	he misses
5. I mix	they _____
6. I catch	she _____

To form the past tense of regular verbs, add –ed or –d:

cook – cooked   jump – jumped

If a verb ends with a silent –e, add –d.

love – loved   smile – smiled

If a verb ends with a consonant and –y, change the –y to –i and add –ed:

copy – copied   study – studied

If the verb ends with a vowel and a consonant, double the consonant and add –ed:

hop – hopped   step – stepped

Write the simple past tense form of each verb.

smile	chop	hop
smiled		

copy	plant	supply

study	walk	clap

stay	dance	love

Past Tense of Irregular Verbs
These verbs do not add –ed or –d to form the past tense.
Some verbs change the vowel, other verbs change
completely, and a few others do not change at all.

Listen and read the verbs.

Present	Past	Past Participle	Present	Past	Past Participle
break	broke	broken	buy	bought	bought
bring	brought	brought	get	got	gotten
come	came	come	have	had	had
do	did	done	sing	sang	sung
drive	drove	driven	swim	swam	swum
eat	ate	eaten	understand	understood	understood
give	gave	given	wear	wore	worn

Complete each sentence with the given verb in the past tense. Then listen and check your answers.

Example: I did my homework after school yesterday. (do)

1. Susie _____ too much ice cream last weekend. (eat)
2. The children _____ in the choir last Sunday. (sing)
3. The boys _____ the glass while playing football. (break)
4. Mr. Porter _____ his new suit to the meeting. (wear)
5. My mother _____ the car to the carwash. (drive)
6. Richard _____ in the swimming competition and won. (swim)
7. I _____ to school early this morning. (come)
8. She _____ a computer for Christmas. (get)

Present	Past	Past Participle	Present	Past	Past Participle
begin	began	begun	meet	met	met
blow	blew	blown	put	put	put
choose	chose	chosen	ring	rang	rung
cut	cut	cut	sit	sat	sat
feel	felt	felt	speak	spoke	spoken
hang	hung	hung	stand	stood	stood
lay	laid	laid	tear	tore	torn
leave	left	left	wake	woke	woke

Find the past tense of the verbs above in the word search below.

```
a  w  e  n  t  b  c  f  d  t  h  r  e  w  e  m  f  g
b  c  a  u  g  h  t  e  h  i  b  e  g  a  n  j  e  k
g  l  l  m  h  n  o  l  a  p  q  t  x  u  c  v  d  t
r  m  e  y  z  u  a  t  b  w  r  c  e  d  r  a  n  k
e  n  m  w  l  s  n  k  j  y  o  s  u  h  w  g  f  s
w  o  p  r  f  l  e  g  t  r  s  k  d  t  c  s  b  t
q  g  h  a  i  e  j  u  v  t  k  f  e  r  t  p  a  o
l  r  m  n  o  p  q  c  h  o  s  e  o  n  m  o  l  o
a  o  a  s  u  t  l  w  v  o  w  d  g  h  i  k  j  d
i  d  y  n  z  a  e  d  f  k  s  x  y  z  a  e  b  c
d  e  c  d  g  e  f  g  h  w  a  s  i  s  a  w  j  k
h  e  l  d  l  m  t  n  o  p  t  q  w  r  o  t  e  r
s  t  o  l  e  x  i  t  h  o  u  g  h  t  y  a  c  e
u  v  j  t  o  r  e  k  l  n  m  b  p  u  t  z  d  t
```

How to play:

Play in pairs. Have pencils and paper ready. After cutting out all the cards, shuffle your partner's cards with yours and place them face down. In turn, each player takes a verb card and writes down the past tense of the verb on his/her piece of paper. The other player checks the answer. If it is correct, the player scores one point. The first player to reach 20 points is the winner. Play again. But this time, for each verb card write a complete sentence in the past tense. Note: Study the lesson on page 27 before you play this game.

go	bring	grow	sit
run	eat	begin	wear
take	buy	get	have
give	drink	choose	do
understand	write	blow	swim
hold	see	feel	sing

Present	Past	Past Participle	Present	Past	Past Participle
catch	caught	caught	run	ran	run
drink	drank	drunk	see	saw	seen
feed	fed	fed	sleep	slept	slept
go	went	gone	steal	stole	stolen
grow	grew	grown	take	took	taken
hold	held	held	think	thought	thought
is	was	been	throw	threw	thrown
ride	rode	ridden	write	wrote	written

Listen and read the verbs.

Go back to the word search, page 24, and find the past tense of the verbs above.

Write sentences in the past tense using the verbs in parentheses.

Example: (grow) Sammy grew two inches this year.

1. (write) _____
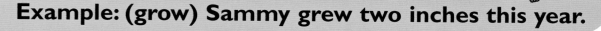
2. (take) _____

3. (go) _____

4. (run) _____

5. (eat) _____

6. (see) _____

7. (sleep) _____

8. (drink) _____

9. (feed) _____

10. (ride) _____

When the verb to be, in any of its forms, is used by itself, it is called a linking verb.

She _is_ pretty.

When the verb to be, in any of its forms, is used with another verb, it is called a helping or auxiliary verb.

She _is_ going to a party.

helping verb   main verb

For each sentence, write if the verb to be is used as a linking verb or a helping verb.

Example: This is a mask.   linking

1. I am wearing a new jacket. _____

2. They were playing chess after school. _____

3. I was eating a hot dog for lunch. _____

4. You are using my favorite pencil. _____

5. That is my favorite book. _____

6. Jack is leaving as soon as possible. _____

7. Mary is bored with the talent show. _____

8. Josephine was in the back yard. _____

9. Robert was playing in the back yard. _____

10. Patrick and Anthony are going to summer camp. _____

11. The children were away at summer camp. _____

12. The twins are watching T.V. in their bedroom. _____

Listen, then circle the helping verb and underline the main verb in each sentence.

Example: The students (are) <u>finishing</u> their monthly exams.

1. The dog is running after the cat.

2. The scientist is working in his laboratory.

3. The students are studying their English lesson.

4. The spacecraft is flying very fast.

5. Robert is making a model ship.

6. She is talking to her teacher.

7. Mr. Rivers is washing his car.

8. The teachers are preparing their final exams.

Write sentences using is, am, or are as a helping verb.

1. _____

2. _____

3. _____

4. _____

5. _____

6. _____

The verb to have is a main verb, but we also use it as a helping or auxiliary verb in the present perfect and past perfect tenses.

Present perfect

Have you washed the dishes?
Yes, I have./No, I haven't.
Has she finished her homework?
Yes, she has./No, she hasn't.

Past perfect

Had you been there before?
Yes, I had./No, I hadn't.
Had they seen the movie before?
Yes, they had./No, they hadn't.

In each sentence, underline the correct option.

Example: She have/<u>had</u> baked cookies.

1. Mary has/have jumped that fence before.

2. We has/had bought a different car.

3. Carla has/have tried to call you.

4. The stores have/had closed at 6 o'clock.

5. Our team has/had won six or seven times during the football season.

Listen and check your answers.

The verb to do also acts as a helping or auxiliary verb. We use do to ask questions and to respond with short affirmative or negative answers, in the present or past tense.

Present Tense

Do you play tennis?
Yes, I do./No, I don't.
Does he play football?
Yes, he does./No, he doesn't.

Past Tense

Did you play hockey?
Yes, I did./No, I didn't.
Did they play golf?
Yes, they did./No, they didn't.

In each question, underline the correct option. Then, answer each question with an affirmative or a negative short answer.

Example: Does/<u>Did</u> the boys go out to play?   Yes, they did.

1. Does/Don't Maria help her mother? _____

2. Do/Doesn't Sandra like to dance? _____

3. Do/Did her brother go to the movies? _____

4. Didn't/Do the doctor go to the hospital? _____

5. Does/Do the waitress clean the tables? _____

6. Doesn't/Do the baby go to bed early? _____

Listen and check your answers.

Answer each question with a short affirmative or negative answer using do, does, or did.

Examples: Did the students bring their lunch?
Yes, they did.
Does the teacher come to school early?
No, she doesn't.

1. **Does the waiter deserve a tip?**

   Yes, _____

2. **Did the actress win an Oscar?**

   No, _____

3. **Do the boys want to play football after school?**

   No, _____

4. **Does the news reporter have to take pictures, too?**

   Yes, _____

5. **Did the animals drink water from the river?**

   No, _____

6. **Did the barber cut his hair?**

   No, _____

7. **Does the music teacher play the guitar?**

   Yes, _____

8. **Do the horses exercise every day?**

   Yes, _____

Listen and check your answers.

To write a good factual report, follow these steps:

Choosing a topic

Choose a topic that you are interested in and that will be interesting for other students, too.

Planning your report

Make a list of questions about your chosen topic (Who? What? Where? When? Why? How many? How long?, etc.)

Collecting information

Look for information about your chosen topic in reference books and encyclopedias, at home, and at the school library. Check the internet, too. Take notes of the important facts about your topic. Use a different sheet of paper for each group of ideas. Try to answer the list of questions you made.

Organizing your information

Look at your notes and try to arrange them in order.
Give each group of notes a heading. Decide on the order of your paragraphs.

Writing your report

Write a paragraph about each main idea. Include all the information about that idea in every paragraph.

Mentioning your sources

At the end of your report, write the titles of the books where you obtained information. Include the title of the book, the author, and the publisher.

Checking your report

Read and check your report carefully according to these two checklists:

Organization Checklist

- **Does my report have a title?**
- **Is the report interesting?**
- **Is each paragraph about one main idea?**
- **Does each paragraph have a topic sentence?**
- **Are all the facts in the correct order?**

Style Checklist

- **Have I used a variety of adjectives, verbs, and adverbs?**
- **Are pronouns clear and used correctly?**
- **Does each sentence have a subject and a predicate?**
- **Is each word spelled correctly?**
- **Is my handwriting clear and neat?**

Listen and read the report.

Tortoises and Turtles

Tortoises and turtles are very interesting animals. They belong to the reptile family. They breathe air, have scales, and are cold-blooded, which means that their immediate surroundings affect their body temperature.

There are about 230 kinds of turtles and tortoises living in different parts of the world. They live both on land and in water. The name tortoise is usually given to the kinds that live on land. Those living in water are called turtles.

Both tortoises and turtles have a hard shell where the vertebrae have become attached. When in danger both are able to draw in their head, legs, and tail. Because of this hard shell, tortoises and turtles move slowly.

Tortoises and turtles can vary greatly in color, size, and weight. They can be green, brown, red, black, or yellow. They can be just a few centimeters long and weigh only a few grams, or they can be as long as three meters and weigh over half a ton.

Tortoises are mostly vegetarian, while freshwater turtles eat other small animals or insects. Both hibernate and lay eggs.

Tortoises and turtles have existed for millions of years, and many people believe it may have something to do with their unique shell.

Tortoises and turtles are fascinating animals to observe. Many children today keep small tortoises as pets.

Our World Encyclopedia by Leonard Sealey, Macmillan Education
New Practice Readers by Donald G. Anderson, McGraw-Hill

Carefully read the report and answer the questions.

1. What is the title of the report?

_____

2. How many paragraphs does the report have?

_____

3. What is the topic sentence of the first paragraph?

_____

4. What is the topic sentence of the fourth paragraph?

_____

Write six of the most interesting facts that you learned about tortoises and turtles.

1. _____

2. _____

3. _____

4. _____

5. _____

6. _____

The Heart

Did you know your heart is a muscle about the size of a large fist? Do you know how much a heart weighs? Why is it called the strongest organ in your body? How many times does your heart beat a minute? What is its main function?

Look for information and write a report about the heart. Add an illustration.

Remember the rules for writing a good report.

A. Complete each sentence with the given verb in the past tense.

Example: She wore a new hat at the wedding last week. (wear)

1. She _____ a beautiful old French song. (sing)

2. My mom _____ from Chicago to New Orleans. (drive)

3. The children _____ all morning in the pool. (swim)

4. He fell and _____ his knee. (cut)

5. You _____ the fish back into the lake. (throw)

B. Write sentences in the past tense with the given verbs.

1. (drink)
_____

2. (take)
_____

3. (steal)
_____

4. (choose)
_____

5. (hang)
_____

C. Underline the correct option in each question.
Then answer with a short affirmative or negative answer.

Example: Does/<u>Did</u> the girls bake a cake?
No, they didn't.

1. Does/Do Bob's grandmother live with them?

   No, _____

2. Did/Do the doctor arrive early?

   Yes, _____

3. Didn't/Do your father go to work today?

   Yes, _____

4. Do/Doesn't Marcus like to paint?

   No, _____

D. Answer each question with a short affirmative
or negative answer using do, does, or did.

Example: Does she go to school by bus?
Yes, she does.

1. Did she receive my letter?

   No, _____

2. Do they want to stay for dinner?

   Yes, _____

3. Does your mother have short hair?

   No, _____

E. Look for information about one of the following titles (or choose your own title if you wish) and write a report. Remember the rules for writing a good report. Add an illustration.

- **The Human Skeleton**
- **Hospitals**
- **How to Stay Healthy**
- **Famous Medical Discoveries**

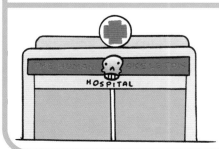

An adjective describes a noun.
It can tell us what kind:
   a strange man   a pretty girl
It can tell us what color:
   a black cat   a yellow coat
It can tell us which one:
   this table   those teachers

Complete each sentence with an appropriate adjective.

1. My best friend has _____ eyes.

2. _____ weather is good for plants.

3. Her _____ hat keeps her warm.

4. We drew a _____ picture.

5. Dad is an _____ tennis player.

6. Our pet dog is a _____ companion.

7. That _____ building is where my father works.

8. Susie has a _____ car.

9. We heard _____ music last night.

10. We saw strange bears and _____ monkeys at the zoo.

Adjectives do not always come before the noun they describe. Sometimes they come after the linking verb to be.

Example: The dress is <u>yellow</u>.
(The adjective yellow describes the dress.)

In each sentence, circle the adjective. Then, after each sentence write the adjective and the noun it describes.

Example: My floor is (clean) .   **clean floor**

1. The teacher was angry.
2. Her potatoes were cold.
3. These sentences are easy.
4. Monica is adorable.
5. The clown was being funny.
6. The horse was hungry.
7. Those movie stars are famous.
8. Father is proud.
9. The flowers were colorful.
10. The ballet dancer is graceful.

_____
_____
_____
_____
_____
_____
_____

Listen and check your answers.

Write five original adjectives that could describe each picture.

1. _____   1. _____   1. _____   1. _____
2. _____   2. _____   2. _____   2. _____
3. _____   3. _____   3. _____   3. _____
4. _____   4. _____   4. _____   4. _____
5. _____   5. _____   5. _____   5. _____

In each sentence, underline the adjectives and circle the nouns they describe.

Example: I have a <u>new</u> (puppy).

1. The brave fireman rescued the small children.

2. Susie's brothers are tall and thin.

3. The handsome man married the beautiful lady.

4. The delicious cookies were on the yellow plate.

5. Your tennis shoes look newer than mine.

6. The young children liked the sandy beach.

7. The funny clowns climbed out of the tiny car.

8. Many people went to the races last Saturday.

9. The longest race of the day was very exciting.

10. The mysterious spaceship landed in the forest.

We use comparative adjectives to compare two nouns.
To form the comparative adjective, we add –er.
In comparative sentences we use than.

     This cat is smaller than that cat.

We use superlative adjectives to compare three or more nouns.
To form the superlative adjective, we add –est.

     He is the tallest boy in the room.

Spelling Rules

With adjectives that end with an –e, just add –r for the comparative and –st for the superlative.

    large   larger   largest

With adjectives that end with a consonant and a –y, change the –y to –i and add –er or –est.

    silly   sillier   silliest

With adjectives that end in a single consonant and a single vowel, double the final consonant and add –er or –est.

    big   bigger   biggest

Irregular adjectives

    good   better   best
    bad   worse   worst

In each sentence, underline the correct form of the adjective.

Example: Susie is the older/<u>oldest</u> girl in the class.

1. His report was the longer/longest of his class.
2. The kitchen is the warmer/warmest room in the house.
3. Yesterday was colder/coldest than today.
4. My desk is neater/neatest than Mary's.
5. I want the smaller/smallest bicycle in the store.

Listen and check your answers.

Write comparative and superlative sentences using the given adjectives.

Example: (easy) Science is easier for me than Math.
Science for me is the easiest subject of all.

1. (pretty) _____

_____

2. (clean) _____

_____

3. (happy) _____

_____

4. (young) _____

_____

To form **comparative** and **superlative adjectives** with words of three or more syllables, we do not use **–er** and **–est**. For comparatives, use **more** and **than**:

> Sammy is **more** intelligent **than** Robert.

For superlatives, use **the most**:

> Susie is **the most** intelligent of all the students.

Complete each sentence with the correct form of the given adjective.

Example: This is the most expensive toy in the store. (expensive)

1. This ring is _____ than that one. (expensive)

2. She is the _____ girl in the class. (intelligent)

3. This year's concert was _____ than last year's. (good)

4. That was an _____ movie. (interesting)

5. In area, Canada is _____ than Mexico. (large)

6. That was the _____ story I've ever read. (scary)

7. This car is _____ than that one. (small)

8. That was the _____ hamburger I've ever tasted! (bad)

9. Her handwriting is _____ than mine. (neat)

10. This test was _____ than the Science test. (difficult)

Listen and check your answers.

We use adverbs to give more information about a verb or an adjective.

Adverbs can tell us about how, where, or when.

how adverbs

slowly   carefully   badly

where adverbs

inside   below   away

when adverbs

later   today   now

Write how, where, or when after each adverb.

1. carefully _____
2. away _____
3. inside _____
4. neatly _____
5. early _____
6. fast _____
7. below _____

8. here _____
9. slowly _____
10. today _____
11. under _____
12. yearly _____
13. outside _____
14. noisily _____

Listen and check your answers.

Circle the adverb in each sentence.

Example: The trained dogs jumped (quickly) through the ring of fire.

1. He went below to see if he could fix the washing machine.

2. The children go yearly to their summer camps.

3. The mothers watched eagerly as their children performed.

47

Complete each sentence with an appropriate adverb of the given type.

Example: The taxi is here.   (where)

1. The children sang _____ .   (how)
2. We'll be leaving _____ .   (when)
3. Our family goes on a vacation _____ . (when)
4. We ran _____ down to the mall.   (how)
5. I was studying my Math _____ .   (when)
6. She paid the man _____ .   (how)
7. He got up _____ .   (how)
8. My teacher wrote _____ on the blackboard. (how)
9. The boys rode _____ on their bikes.   (when)
10. The children went to the library _____ .   (when)
11. I am going to the zoo _____ .   (when)
12. Mary wrote her report _____ .   (where)

Write sentences using the kind of adverb given in parentheses.

1. (when) _____

_____
2. (how) _____

_____
3. (where) _____

_____

In each sentence, underline the adverb and circle the verb. Then, write each verb and adverb under the correct heading.

	Verb	Adverb
1. I washed my car today.	___	___
2. Suddenly, it started to rain.	___	___
3. The child used the scissors carefully.	___	___
4. The soldiers fought bravely.	___	___
5. We finished our pizza quickly.	___	___
6. I baked cookies yesterday.	___	___
7. He goes to his weekly swimming lessons.	___	___
8. The twins threw the toys everywhere.	___	___
9. The mouse ran swiftly out of its hole.	___	___
10. My cousin came early to get me.	___	___
11. Sammy took his sister outside.	___	___
12. Lucy often has riding lessons.	___	___

Listen and check your answers.

Label each sentence, according to the following key.
- n. noun
- adj. adjective
- v. verb
- p. pronoun
- adv. adverb
- art. article

Example: art. adj. n. v. adv.

The little girl ran outside.

1. We feed the dogs regularly.

2. Charles wrote them a letter.

3. They have a small kitten.

4. The new toys were everywhere.

5. The children are going swimming today.

6. Several thirsty children drank cold lemonade.

7. Mother washed the dishes carefully.

8. That tiny baby is sleeping soundly.

9. They wrote their letters to Santa yesterday.

10. The doctors looked outside.

11. The policeman ran quickly after the car thieves.

12. Suddenly, the rain started!

The Descriptive Paragraph

A good descriptive paragraph creates a vivid image in the mind of the reader. It is a picture in words. A descriptive paragraph uses words and phrases that appeal to the reader's five senses (sight, hearing, smell, taste, and touch). This makes the description seem more real to the reader.

Listen and read the paragraph.

Last weekend I went with my mom and my little sister to our winter cabin near the lake. We left on Friday afternoon. The sky looked like a dark blue canvas with huge fluffy clouds painted on it. By the time we arrived at the lake, snowflakes were falling. They felt like cool bee stings on our faces. Jenny, my sister, put her tongue out to catch some flakes.

Jenny and I played outside in the snow while my mom went into the cabin. Soon, we smelled the delicious aroma of hot chocolate coming from the kitchen window. Suddenly, we both felt cold and hungry.

We went inside, took off our coats and our heavy, wet boots, and sat down by the fire. Thick logs were burning in the fireplace. They made a gentle crackling sound. We sat quietly with our hands cupped around the big steaming mugs of hot chocolate. It was a nice way to start the weekend.

Complete the table with examples of details which appeal to the senses.

sight	
hearing	
smell	
taste	
touch	

Paste a picture from a magazine. Discuss it with a partner and then write a descriptive paragraph about it. Use words that will appeal to the reader's five senses.

Picture

A. Complete each sentence with an appropriate adjective.

1. My brother has a _____ bicycle.

2. His _____ coat keeps him very warm in the winter.

3. My neighbor has a _____ car.

4. We saw some very _____ monkeys at the zoo.

B. In each sentence, underline the adjectives and circle the nouns they describe.

1. The young man married the pretty girl from the shoe store.

2. All the young children enjoyed the funny movie.

3. A cold wind blew through the tall trees.

4. The old man doesn't like silly stories.

C. In each sentence, underline the correct form of the adjective.

1. The bathroom is the smaller/smallest room in the house.

2. His shoes are dirtier/dirtiest than mine.

3. Her report was the best/better report in the whole class.

4. Last month was wetter/wettest than this month.

5. Billy is the more intelligent/most intelligent boy in the class.

D. Complete each sentence with the correct form of the given adjective.

1. That was a _____ movie. (fascinating)

2. That was the _____ story I've ever heard! (funny)

3. This exam was _____ than the last one. (difficult)

4. This cake is _____ than the other one we made. (good)

5. It's the _____ T.V. in the store. (expensive)

6. She is a very _____ girl and very smart too. (pretty)

7. It's the _____ soup I've ever tasted! (bad)

8. This dog is _____ than your dog. (dirty)

E. Complete each sentence with an appropriate adverb of the given type.

Example: The bus will leave soon. (when)

1. It was hot so we had our lunch _____ . (where)

2. We're all going to the zoo _____ . (when)

3. They all ran _____ down the street. (how)

4. We're going on vacation _____ . (when)

5. The man went _____ . (where)

6. The baby shouted _____ for his mother. (how)

F. Look for information and write a report about spiders.

How much do you know about spiders? Many people think that spiders are insects. Insects have six legs while spiders have eight. Spiders have only two body parts, the head and the abdomen, while insects have three. Did you know that all spiders produce milk? Do you know why? Do you know how different spiders catch their food?

Contractions are made by joining two words into a shorter word. An apostrophe is used in place of the missing letter.

I am → I'm
I have → I've
do not → don't
cannot → can't

I am	I'm	I have	I've	I will	I'll
you are	you're	you have	you've	you will	you'll
he is	he's	he has	he's	he will	he'll
she is	she's	she has	she's	she will	she'll
it is	it's	it has	it's	it will	it'll
we are	we're	we have	we've	we will	we'll
they are	they're	they have	they've	they will	they'll
are not	aren't	have not	haven't	will not	won't
is not	isn't	has not	hasn't	did not	didn't
cannot	can't	must not	mustn't	I would	I'd
do not	don't	does not	doesn't		
where is	where's	there is	there's		

Write the correct contraction for each pair of words.

is not _____	they are _____	has not _____
I have _____	does not _____	she is _____
cannot _____	I will _____	he is _____
you are _____	we are _____	I am _____
I would _____	have not _____	where is _____
will not _____	he will _____	we will _____
there is _____	must not _____	are not _____
it is _____	it will _____	she will _____

Listen and check your answers.

57

Rewrite each sentence using the correct contraction.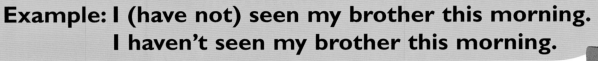

Example: I (have not) seen my brother this morning.
         I haven't seen my brother this morning.

1. He (did not) get any help from the teacher.

_____

2. We (have not) gone to the movies lately.

_____

3. They (cannot) go to the party wearing jeans.

_____

4. (I will) get your lunch box from the car.

_____

5. She (has not) bought the books you need for that class.

_____

6. (I would) like to go see my grandmother this weekend.

_____

7. My teacher (cannot) get her car started.

_____

8. (I am) sorry I (did not) study for the exam.

_____

Write sentences using contractions.

1. (I will) _____

2. (where is) _____

3. (we will) _____

4. (have not) _____

5. (must not) _____

Some words are made by putting two different words together. The new words are called compound words.

Example: grape + fruit = grapefruit

Complete each word with another word from the box to form a compound word.

1. high _____
2. birth _____
3. home _____
4. pea _____
5. sun _____

6. base _____
7. toe _____
8. sail _____
9. play _____
10. hair _____

shine	nut
work	day
boat	brush
way	ball
nail	ground

Write the new words below.

1. _____
2. _____
3. _____
4. _____
5. _____

6. _____
7. _____
8. _____
9. _____
10. _____

Listen and check your answers.

Write as many more compound words as you can think of.

_____ _____ _____

_____ _____ _____

_____ _____ _____

Add one word to each group of words to form compound words and then write the new words in the spaces.

Example: school

class + room = classroom

bed bedroom

schoolroom

1. work
   note   + _____ = _____
   cook   _____

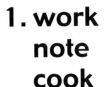

2. fire
   mail   + _____ = _____
   milk   _____

3. drive
   high   + _____ = _____
   free   _____

4. tooth   + _____
   hair   = _____

Write three sentences using any of the compound words above.

1. _____

2. _____

3. _____

A **synonym** is a word that means the same or nearly the same as another word.

single	– one	friends	– companions	
brave	– courageous	put	– place	
happy	– glad	cost	– price	
frightened	– scared	under	– below	
reduce	– lessen	begin	– start	
thief	– burglar	smart	– intelligent	
error	– mistake	speak	– talk	

I'm smart and intelligent!

Rewrite each sentence using a synonym for the underlined word, and make other necessary changes.

Example: The girl was very <u>brave</u> to rescue the baby.
The girl was very courageous to rescue the baby.

1. There was an <u>error</u> in the spelling test.

2. The <u>cost</u> of that coat is outrageous.

3. The fish are swimming <u>under</u> the bridge.

4. The children were very <u>happy</u> to find the hidden treasure.

5. All her <u>friends</u> went to her birthday party.

6. The <u>intelligent</u> rabbit ran to its hole.

7. The loud noise <u>scared</u> the baby.

8. My father works very hard. He should <u>lessen</u> his workload.

Listen and check your answers.

61

In each line of words underline three synonyms. If you see a word that you don't recognize, look it up in the dictionary.

Example: strong   <u>thin</u>   <u>slender</u>   tall   <u>skinny</u>

1. orderly   successful   neat   tidy   slow

2. happy   delighted   pretty   noisy   glad

3. quiet   rapid   fast   smart   quick

4. build   play   erect   erase   construct

5. prepare   acquire   receive   get   arrange

6. uneven   unusual   whole   entire   complete

7. utter   speak   grow   declare   play

8. dirty   neat   soiled   clean   filthy

9. yell   speak   whisper   scream   shout

10. stand   wander   roam   stray   pull

11. single   one   several   only   many

12. carry   set   place   push   put

13. grow   stretch   lessen   decrease   reduce

14. sort   unite   blend   mix   sift

15. mean   pretty   ugly   lovely   beautiful

16. need   want   play   desire   succeed

Listen and check your answers.

A. Rewrite each sentence using the correct contraction.

1. She (has not) done her homework.

_____

2. You (cannot) go outside without your coat.

_____

3. The car (will not) start.

_____

4. They (did not) play baseball after school.

_____

5. You (are not) on the team this season.

_____

B. Complete each sentence with a compound word from the box.

freeway	fireman	homework	baseball
cookbook	hairbrush	birthday	playground

1. I can't find my comb and my _____.

2. Mom, can you help me with my _____, please?

3. All the kids are playing outside in the _____.

4. My uncle is a _____. He's very brave.

5. This _____ contains some wonderful recipes.

6. Is today your _____? Happy birthday!

7. There was an accident on the _____ last week.

8. He's lucky. He lives right next to the _____ stadium.

C. Write a synonym for each word.

1. big – _____
3. happy – _____
5. rapid – _____

2. mistake – _____
4. pretty – _____
6. intelligent – _____

D. Write an antonym for each word.

1. night – _____
5. difficult – _____
9. white – _____

2. cold – _____
6. begin – _____
10. big – _____

3. tall – _____
7. young – _____

4. present – _____
8. difficult – _____

E. Write a homophone for each word.

1. sun – _____
3. for – _____
5. weak – _____

2. hour – _____
4. eight – _____
6. aunt – _____

F. Write sentences using synonyms, antonyms, and homophones.

1. _____

2. _____

3. _____

4. _____

5. _____

6. _____

Common prepositions include: after, from, near, at, to, during, for, through, over, between, with, etc. A prepositional phrase begins with a preposition and ends with a noun or pronoun that is called the object of the preposition.

The boys jumped <u>into the lake</u>.

Underline the prepositional phrase in each sentence and write the object of each preposition.

Example: The birds flew directly <u>into the rain</u>. rain

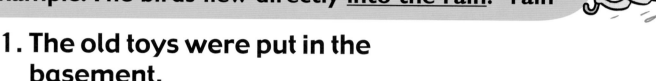

1. The old toys were put in the basement.

2. My sister went shopping with my aunt.

3. Our winter cabin is near a lake.

4. Bears hibernate during the winter.

5. We ran toward him.

6. The boys saw their footprints in the sand.

7. During autumn, the trees lose their leaves.

8. The plane flew over the sea.

9. Susie sat under the tree and read her book.

10. The helicopter flew over the city.

Listen and check your answers.

Prepositional phrases **can be used to combine two sentences.**

Example: The boys went to the farm.
The boys went at night.
The boys went to the farm at night.

Combine the following sentences.

1. I read at night.
   I read before going to bed.

   _____

2. The girls walked through the mall.
   The girls walked to the store.

   _____

3. The doctors looked at the patient.
   The doctors looked in his bed.

   _____

4. He saw thousands of stars.
   He saw them across the sky.

   _____

5. The teacher looked for the pencils.
   The teacher looked in their desks.

   _____

6. Robert stood under the tree.
   Robert stood below the falling leaves.

   _____

Listen and check your answers.

Listen and read the following prepositions.

across – around – behind – beside – between – from – in
inside – near – on – outside – over – through – to – toward
along – until – up – with – above – after – before – below
down – about – of – into – for – by – at – among

Circle the 32 prepositions in the word search.

```
W I T H B C F R O M D E F G O U T S I D E H J
M G O P Q R S T B U V W X Y A Z A C B D F J A
O D E A B O U T F E G A F T E R H J K E L M N
V Q R S C V W Z A B S C J K L M O F P Q L N R
E H U F O R X T F D E I N T O F H U G T U O V
R T S R Q P O N O N M L D K J H G E N E D C W
A B W V U T R S L P Q M N E O P Q R S D V B C
Y A P C F H J K S O J A B O V E L M T U X U Z
U B E G B E T W E E N E F T H R O U G H G P H
K N A B D F D A D O W N A C B E B J C K D T E
Y Z T L M G B N C A T P D N E A R P Q B Y R S
X D B I C H E D P Q O F F G H J I K L M N P R
U W T K L M F N O R G X H Y I N S I D E L Q S
E P Q R S T O W A R D E W Z N V U A M O N G T
O T M L K J R H G S Z A B F D E I S H L N Q S
A F B U V W E X Y T A L O N G C N J K M E R Z
```

Write sentences with any of the above prepositions.

1. _____
2. _____
3. _____

Bravo!   Help!   Ouch!   Hooray!   Oh dear!
Surprise!   Excellent!   Wow!   Oh no!   Whew!   Ah!

An interjection is a word to express surprise, fear, relief, joy, anger, or other strong feelings. An interjection is followed by an exclamation point (!).
The first word following the exclamation point is the start of a new sentence and so it begins with a capital letter.

Whew! What a relief.   Help! I can't stop.
Ouch! That hurt.   Oh no! I forgot my money.

Circle the interjection in each sentence.

1. Surprise! Here is your birthday cake.
2. Our team won the game. Hooray! Hooray!
3. Ouch! I hurt my finger with the hammer.
4. Ah! I caught you eating the candy.

Listen and repeat the sentences.

Write sentences using the interjections at the top of the page.

1. _____
   _____

2. _____
   _____

3. _____
   _____

4. _____
   _____

Conjunctions (or connectors) connect words or groups of words.

Three common conjunctions are and, but, and or:

and is used to express addition

    Mary and Robert went outside to play.

but is used to express contrast

    She wanted to buy candy, but didn't have any money.

or is used to express choice

    Do you want your cake with chocolate or vanilla ice cream?

No Car.

Circle the conjunction in each sentence and write addition, contrast, or choice after each sentence.

Example: He wanted to drive the car, but Dad wouldn't let him.   contrast

1. Our rainy season is usually in June or July.

2. We could go swimming, but the water is too cold.

3. Peter asked us to take sodas or sandwiches to the party.

4. I did my homework with Alex and Margaret.

5. He needed a pen or a pencil to finish the test.

6. I need a new bathing suit, but I can't find one in my size.

Complete each sentence with or, and, or but.

1. She wanted to go to the party _____ her mom wouldn't let her.

2. I need some paint _____ some paintbrushes to do the job.

3. My mother _____ father went shopping.

4. What do you prefer, apples _____ pears?

5. I'd like to go out _____ I have a lot of work to do.

6. We can see the movie on Friday _____ Saturday. You choose.

Listen and check your answers.

72

Conjunctions are also used to make one long sentence out of two short ones.

(Remember that a comma is used before but.)

Snow and sleet began to fall. Fortunately, we were already at home.

Snow and sleet began to fall, but fortunately we were already at home.

Combine each pair of short sentences into one longer sentence using or, and, or but.

Example: We enjoyed the picnic.
The mosquitos were terrible.
We enjoyed the picnic, but
the mosquitos were terrible.

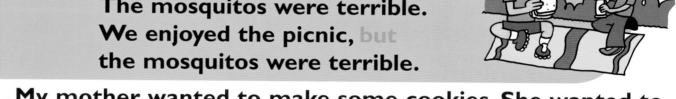

1. My mother wanted to make some cookies. She wanted to make some cakes.

_____

_____

2. The soup was delicious. It was too hot to eat.

_____

_____

3. Do you want to go to the movies? Do you want to go to the park?

_____

_____

4. The whole family sat down in the living room. They all watched T.V.

_____

_____

Listen and check your answers.

A. Underline the prepositional phrase in each sentence and write the object of each preposition.

Example: <u>After a noisy discussion</u>, the men left. discussion

1. The clown told funny stories to the children. _____

2. The ostrich ran between the trees. _____

3. The teacher jumped into the taxi. _____

4. The doctor will be here in a minute. _____

5. My sister likes to go shopping with my mother. _____

6. Robert wasn't careful and ran into the table. _____

B. Write six interjections.

_____ _____ _____

_____ _____ _____

C. Write four sentences using an interjection.

1. _____
2. _____
3. _____
4. _____

D. Circle the conjunction in each sentence, and after each sentence write addition, contrast, or choice.

1. The baby wanted his milk and cookies. _____

2. I don't know if I should do my homework tonight or early tomorrow. _____

3. His grandparents wanted to visit him, but he had the measles. _____

4. The doctor gave the patient an injection and some medicine. _____

E. Combine each pair of short sentences into one longer sentence using the conjunction but.

1. My mother is very strict. She is fair.

_____

2. Robert wants to go to the movies. He doesn't have any money.

_____

3. I like horses. I am afraid to get on them.

_____

4. The teacher explained the lesson. The student didn't understand.

_____

F. Write sentences using and, or, or but.

1. _____

2. _____

G. Read about bees. Then look up information about bees and write a report. Remember to follow the steps for writing a report. Paste or draw an illustration.

Did you know that bees live in a colony? Did you know that bees work so hard that they actually kill themselves working? A worker bee works for about six weeks and then dies. This does not affect the colony because a young worker bee immediately takes his place. Do you know why bees work so hard? Do you know what they produce?

The **future simple tense** is one of the tenses used to indicate an action in a time to come, as in predictions, offers, and conditions.

The auxiliary verb **will** is used with the principal verb to form the future simple tense.

Mary **will** write an excellent report.

I **will** cook supper if...

Rewrite each sentence in the future tense.

Example: He (leave) early tomorrow on the 9 o'clock train.

He will leave early tomorrow on the 9 o'clock train.

1. We (see) him at school in the morning.

_____

2. He (be) here in a few minutes.

_____

3. The janitor (clean) the school after classes.

_____

4. Mr. Johnson's wife (buy) the sodas and sandwiches for the party.

_____

5. Our friends (meet) us at the shopping center.

_____

6. Mrs. Smith (fly) to San Antonio next week.

_____

7. Dr. Brown (speak) to the children about cleaning
   their teeth.

_____

8. The girls (go) to the movies after school.

_____

9. The dog (obey) his trainer and do many tricks.

_____

10. My father (wash) his car on Saturday.

_____

11. I (bake) cookies for the Girl Scouts.

_____

Listen and check your answers.

Write five sentences of your own in the future tense.

1. _____

2. _____

3. _____

4. _____

5. _____

When changing a future tense sentence to a question, remember the cross rule. (The auxiliary verb goes to the beginning of the sentence.)

He will go with his mother to the movies.

Will he go with his mother to the movies?

Change each sentence to a question.

Example: We will eat lunch with Peter.

Will we eat lunch with Peter?

1. John will go to school with his sister.

2. The Wilsons will fly to Spain on vacation.

3. Susie will write an excellent report on elephants.

4. My friend Edward will wear his new coat.

5. Her secretary will go to her office at 9:00 a.m.

6. The girls will play with their dolls in the tree house.

7. Dr. Jones will examine his patient at 4:00 p.m.

8. The policeman will catch the thief who stole the jewels.

Listen and check your answers.

Affirmative

I will go very soon.

She will study for her exam.

They will have a party.

Negative

I won't (will not) go very soon.

She won't (will not) study for her exam.

They won't (will not) have a party.

OF COURSE, I WILL STUDY...

...NOT

Rewrite each sentence in the negative form.

1. I will mail the letter tomorrow.

2. The president will speak to the governor.

3. We will eat dinner at seven–thirty tonight.

4. Mrs. Smith will meet us at the library.

5. The baby will drink his milk after his nap.

6. The boys will go to the baseball game on Saturday.

7. My teacher will check all of our homework after school.

Listen and check your answers.

To form the future tense with going to:

(to be) + going to + main verb

Use it to talk about people's plans:

    I am going to finish my report next week.

    He is going to learn to speak English.

Rewrite each sentence using going to.

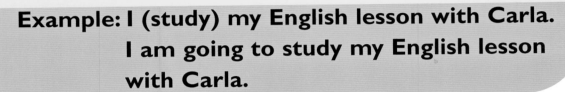

Example: I (study) my English lesson with Carla.

    I am going to study my English lesson with Carla.

1. Mrs. Smith (invite) all of her friends to her birthday party.

_____

2. We (go) to the movies on Saturday.

_____

3. The teacher (help) me with my Math.

_____

4. Tommy (finish) his homework after school.

_____

5. Susie (play) tennis at the club on Sunday.

_____

6. The boys (watch) the baseball game at David's house.

_____

7. The doctors (operate) on the man who was hurt.

_____

8. Robert (invite) Lucy to the movies this week.

_____

9. The children (watch) T.V. after dinner.

_____

10. I (wear) my new dress to the party.

_____

11. The mailman (deliver) the mail early tomorrow.

_____

12. The housekeeper (clean) the house tomorrow.

_____

Listen and check your answers.

Write five sentences talking about people's plans.

1. _____

2. _____

3. _____

4. _____

5. _____

To change going to sentences to questions, use the cross rule.

> The children are going to take an exam.
> Are the children going to take an exam?
> She is going to learn how to swim.
> Is she going to learn how to swim?

Change each sentence to a question.

1. The Browns are going to buy a new car.

2. The workers are going to build a new house.

3. My mother is going to make some cookies.

4. They are going to buy fruit and vegetables.

5. The girls are going to have a big party.

6. Dr. Smith is going to stop by the hospital.

Listen and check your answers.

Affirmative

I'm going to buy a soda.
She is going to go to bed.

They are going to visit Peter.

Negative

I'm not going to buy a soda.
She isn't (is not) going to go to bed.

They aren't (are not) going to visit Peter.

Change each sentence to the negative form. First, write your sentences in the full form. Then, rewrite them using contractions.

Example: I am going to ask my father what to do.
I am not going to ask my father what to do.
I'm not going to ask my father what to do.

1. George is going to work with his uncle.

2. The children are going to listen to the radio.

3. Mr. Brown is going to ride his horse.

4. My mother is going to shop for a new dress.

5. The cooks are going to bake a wedding cake.

Listen and check your answers.

Use some in affirmative sentences.

Example: He has some books on top of his desk.

Use any in negative sentences or in questions.

Examples: He doesn't have any books on top of his desk.
Does he have any books on top of his desk?

Underline the correct option in each sentence.

Example: He doesn't have some/<u>any</u> friends.

1. The policeman found some/any boxes in the trunk of the car.

2. I didn't have some/any money with me.

3. Are there some/any patients waiting to see me?

4. Mrs. Smith doesn't have some/any children.

5. She gave the teacher some/any flowers.

6. My aunt bought some/any apples at the supermarket.

7. He doesn't have some/any pens I can borrow.

8. She doesn't have some/any milk or juice.

9. Did the students have some/any lunch during recess?

Listen and check your answers.

Read the grammar rules.

Use someone, something, and somewhere in affirmative sentences:

Use someone when referring to no one in particular:
    There is someone outside the window.

Use something when referring to no object in particular:
    I can feel something round and soft in my bed.

Use somewhere when referring to no place in particular:
    I want to go somewhere on my Easter vacation.

Use anyone, anything, and anywhere in negative sentences or in questions:

Use anyone when referring to no one in particular:
    Is there anyone in that office?
    I can't see anyone there.

Use anything when referring to no object in particular:
    Is there anything in this box?
    No, there isn't anything in this box.

Use anywhere when referring to no place in particular:
    Do you want to go anywhere special?
    No, I don't want to go anywhere.

Complete each sentence with somewhere, something, someone, anywhere, anything, or anyone.

1. I didn't see _____ in Dr. Smith's office.

2. Robert doesn't know _____ in his new school.

3. I lost my money _____ in my house.

4. There wasn't _____ waiting for me after school.

5. Susie didn't say _____ about the picnic.

6. She isn't going to go _____ this summer.

7. These plants look like _____ from outer space.

8. Doesn't _____ know where the restaurant is?

Write sentences using the given words.

1. (anyone) _____

2. (someone) _____

3. (somewhere) _____

4. (anything) _____

5. (anyone) _____

6. (something) _____

A. Answer each question in the affirmative **and** negative **forms.**

Example: Will you come to my house on Saturday?
         Yes, I will.
         No, I won't.

1. Will Susie help her mother set the table?

_____

_____

2. Will the janitor clean the school in the afternoons?

_____

_____

3. Will they eat dinner at 8 o'clock?

_____

_____

B. Write questions using will **and the given verb.**

Example: (learn) Will the baby learn to sing that song?

1. (run) _____

2. (watch) _____

3. (buy) _____

4. (get) _____

5. (bring) _____

C. Rewrite each sentence in the future tense using going to.

1. The teacher helps me with my Math.

_____

2. The nurse takes a taxi to the hospital.

_____

3. Robert and Peter meet in the library.

_____

4. The squirrels hide in the trees.

_____

5. My aunt gets her hair cut at the beauty salon.

_____

6. Jack invites Mary to the movies.

_____

D. Write three negative sentences using going to.

1. _____

2. _____

3. _____

E. Write three questions using going to.

1. _____

2. _____

3. _____

F. Complete each sentence with some or any.

1. The plumber found _____ leaks in the bathroom.

2. She gave the children _____ cookies.

3. I don't have _____ sugar for my coffee.

4. The girls found _____ nuts under the trees.

5. He doesn't know _____ teacher that teaches dancing.

6. Does he have _____ books I can borrow?

7. She doesn't lend _____ of her books.

G. Write sentences using the given words.

1. (something) _____

2. (anyone) _____

3. (somewhere) _____

4. (anywhere) _____

5. (someone) _____

H. Look for information and write a report about penguins. Draw or paste an illustration.

> **Where do penguins live?**
> **How are they protected from the cold?**
> **Do they live in the water?**
> **Do penguins build their nests anywhere they like?**
> **How many eggs do they lay?**

Penguins

We use the present progressive **tense to describe an action that is happening at the present moment and in a planned future.**

To form the present progressive:
     to be + verb + –ing

Verb spelling changes

If the verb ends with a –y**, add** –ing**:**
     cry – crying   stay – staying

If the verb ends with a single vowel and a consonant, double the consonant and add –ing**:**
     hit – hitting   stop – stopping

If the verb ends with a silent –e**, replace it with** –ing**:**
     give – giving   make – making

Rewrite each sentence in the present progressive.

Example: He (smoke) a lot.
           He is smoking a lot.

1. The teacher (write) the homework on the blackboard.

2. I can't go home because it (rain) very hard.

3. He (have) lunch with James.

4. They are (drive) to New York.

5. She (play) dolls with her cousin.

6. The boys (run) after the football on the playground.

7. The mailman (deliver) all the mail that arrived yesterday.

8. The architect (build) us a new house.

Listen and check your answers.

We use the past progressive:

when we want to talk about an action which was taking place in the past:

> I was working.
>
> The boys were playing.
>
> It was snowing.

When we want to describe an action which was interrupted by another action:

> The man was sleeping in his room when the letter arrived.

To form the past progressive:

> was/were + verb + –ing

Rewrite each sentence using the past progressive. WaaaHHH!

Example: I (sleep) when the baby began to cry.

> I was sleeping when the baby began to cry.

1. He (drive) his car to the garage when the policeman stopped him.

_____

2. The sun (shine) when I got to school.

_____

3. The patients (suffer) greatly when the doctor arrived.

_____

4. John (study) when his father came home.

_____

5. My mother (prepare) dinner when the baby woke up.

_____

6. The architect (build) a new house when the earthquake hit.

_____

7. The girls (sit) by the T.V. when the lights went out.

_____

8. Mark (ask) Roberta to dance when the music stopped.

_____

Listen and check your answers.

Write sentences using the past progressive tense.

1. _____

2. _____

3. _____

4. _____

5. _____

6. _____

7. _____

8. _____

cause = the thing that makes something happen
the reason why something happens

effect = what happens as a result of a particular cause

To relate a cause and an effect, we use connectors like so or that's why:

> The dog was barking all night.
> That's why we couldn't sleep.
> There was no milk in the fridge,
> so I went out to buy some more.

Match each cause with an appropriate effect from the box.

• That's why I'm not feeling very well.
• so we're fixing up the guest room.

• so I don't think we'll play outside.
• That's why he feels tired now.

1. My cousins are coming to stay, _____
2. Bob worked really hard all day. _____
3. I just ate four hot dogs. _____
4. It's snowing, _____

Listen and check your answers.

After each sentence write an appropriate effect.
Use so or that's why.

1. I forgot to put on a sweater. _____
2. Our T.V. broke last night, _____
3. We ran out of milk, _____
4. The patient couldn't sleep. _____

Use because to state the reason for a specific action.
We couldn't watch the movie because the VCR was broken.

Complete each sentence with because.

Example: I couldn't go to school because
I have the measles.

1. I couldn't sleep last night
_____

2. The policeman was angry
_____

3. I didn't do my homework
_____

4. We ran to school
_____

5. The boys took off their jackets
_____

Answer each question with a reason using because.

1. Why didn't you invite me to go to the movies?
Because... _____

2. Why don't you like The Simpsons?
Because... _____

3. Why don't you like horses?
Because... _____

4. Why didn't you like the movie Titanic?
Because... _____

Use say in sentences where the person receiving the information is not mentioned:

> She says she wants to be a movie star.
> He said they were going to the movies.

Use tell in sentences where the person receiving the information is mentioned:

> Billy tells me someone broke the store window.
> John told my father he was going to go for a walk.

Complete each sentence with say or tell in the correct tense.

Example: Mother <u>said</u> she was too busy to go.

1. I _____ them how much I liked my new teacher.

2. She _____ she is going to do her homework.

3. They _____ my father they were going to the library.

4. The teacher _____ us to be quiet and work.

5. He _____ he wants to be a doctor.

6. Her parents _____ the policeman everything.

7. Our principal _____ us to clean up our desks.

8. The secretary _____ she was very tired.

9. The couple _____ they wanted a new apartment.

10. Her grandmother _____ us a story.

Listen and check your answers.

Write sentences with say and tell.

1. _____

2. _____

3. _____

4. _____

5. _____

6. _____

Use the present perfect **tense:**

To talk about actions that began in the past and continue into the present:

I have lived **in France for seven years.**

to talk about completed actions:

We have cleaned **the house.**

and to talk about experiences:

She has flown **in an airplane.**

To form the present perfect tense:

the verb to have **+ the past participle of the verb**

I have studied **English all day.**

He has studied **English all day.**

Some irregular verbs form their past participle by adding –n **or** –en**.**

Present	Past	Past Participle
begin	began	begun
break	broke	broken
bring	brought	brought
buy	bought	bought
catch	caught	caught
come	came	come
do	did	done
drink	drank	drunk
eat	ate	eaten
feed	fed	fed
feel	felt	felt
get	got	gotten
give	gave	given
go	went	gone
grow	grew	grown
have	had	had
hold	held	held
ride	rode	ridden
run	ran	run
see	saw	seen
shake	shook	shaken
sing	sang	sung
sleep	slept	slept
stand	stood	stood
swim	swam	swum
take	took	taken
teach	taught	taught
tell	told	told
think	thought	thought
throw	threw	thrown
wear	wore	worn
win	won	won
write	wrote	written

Rewrite each sentence in the present perfect.

Example: I (sleep) under the tree all afternoon.

          I have slept under the tree all afternoon.

1. She (eat) all of the cookies in the cookie jar.

2. The teacher (taught) the students the lesson.

3. The boys (win) all of the swimming competitions.

4. The doctor (catch) a cold from one of his patients.

5. My aunt (feed) the baby and put him to sleep.

6. The men (see) the baseball game on T.V. six times.

7. The patient (feel) better since Tuesday.

8. Grandfather (go) to see his animals on the farm.

Complete the table with the correct forms of each verb.

Present	Past	Past Participle
drink		
		gone
	came	
	stood	
write		
		grown

Listen and check your answers.

104

Use the past perfect tense to talk about one action in the past which happened before another action, also in the past:

> When we arrived, the ball game had begun.
> Peter had finished before the bell rang.
> My dad had prepared breakfast but no one was hungry.

To form the past perfect:
> had + past participle

Negative form

> The students had not finished the test when the bell rang.
> Johnny had not eaten the cake.

Question form

> Had they finished their homework before they watched T.V.?
> Had she washed her hair before she went to the party?

Rewrite each sentence in the past perfect.

Example: They (sleep) all afternoon before going out.
They had slept all afternoon before going out.

1. They (run) to the barn before the farmer could catch them.

2. My sister (do) her homework when her boyfriend arrived.

3. The mailman (deliver) all the mail before six o'clock.

4. His sister (bring) candy and cookies for the children.

5. The pilot (fly) all over the world but preferred staying at home.

6. The architect (build) many bridges before he was forty years old.

7. The plumber (fix) the refrigerator before my father got home.

8. My cousins (go) home for the holidays.

Listen and check your answers.

Write three sentences using the past perfect.

1.

2.

3.

Present Perfect

Past Perfect

Affirmative

I have eaten.
He has eaten.
They have eaten.

I had eaten.
He had eaten.
They had eaten.

Negative

I haven't (have not) eaten.
He hasn't (has not) eaten.
They haven't (have not) eaten.

I hadn't (had not) eaten.
They hadn't (had not) eaten.
They hadn't (had not) eaten.

Question forms

Present Perfect

Have they seen that movie before?
Has he worked here for many years?

Past Perfect

Had she just woken up from a deep sleep?
Had they visited the zoo many times?

Change each sentence to the interrogative and negative forms.

Example: He has been to New York twice this year.
Has he been to New York twice this year?
He hasn't been to New York twice this year.

1. They had planted many flowers before spring.

_____

_____

2. She has seen all of the old movies.

_____

_____

3. Her husband had already seen the tennis match on T.V.

_____

_____

4. The dog has chased the cat all around the house.

_____

_____

5. The fish have swum around the children for hours.

_____

_____

6. They had practiced all the songs before the concert.

_____

_____

Listen and check your answers.

108

Fill in the rest of the bingo card with the past participles of more verbs.

One student calls out verbs in the present tense. As each verb is called, students place a token on the correct past participle square. The student who completes his/her card first wins the game.

gone				
	sat		grown	
				gotten
eaten			begun	
	worn			taken

A. After each sentence write if it is in the present progressive, past progressive, present perfect, or past perfect tense.

Example: He has eaten seven apples today.

present perfect

1. The children were swimming in the lake. _____

2. The patients have gone to the hospital. _____

3. The couple had wanted twins. _____

4. The teacher is telling everyone to be quiet. _____

5. Grandmother has taken the dog to the farm. _____

6. They had left the airport before I got there. _____

7. My brother was walking the horses. _____

8. The hippos are swimming under the water. _____

B. Complete each sentence with say or tell in the past tense.

1. The teacher _____ the students to be quiet.

2. He _____ all of the boys we were going to the movies.

3. The zoo keeper _____ no one could feed the animals.

4. The nurse _____ the patient had gone home.

5. The couple _____ the doctor they wanted twins.

6. Mark _____ he couldn't go to the movies.

C. Write five sentences in the present perfect tense using the given verbs. Then, change each sentence to the past perfect.

1. (fix) _____

_____

2. (cut) _____

_____

3. (put) _____

_____

4. (come) _____

_____

5. (get) _____

_____

D. Match each statement with an appropriate reason.

1. I am going swimming.
2. I can't see you anymore.
3. He bought a new car.
4. She took a bus.
5. He usually walks to school.
6. They got sick.

- It was cheaper.
- It's too hot.
- His home is very near.
- We moved to another city.
- They ate too much candy.
- He got a raise in pay.

E. Complete each statement with because and a reason.

1. I like Mrs. Miller _____

_____

2. I exercise after school _____

_____

3. I like Saturdays _____

_____

111

F. Look up as much information as you can about dinosaurs, and write a report. Be sure to draw or paste an illustration.

Use between when talking about two persons or things:
> The final play-off in the tennis match will be between Peter and Robert.

Use among when talking about three or more people or objects:
> The crayons were divided among the children.

Complete each sentence using between or among.

1. The hamburgers were divided _____ the football team.

2. The pilot will leave the airport _____ 4:00 and 5:00 in the afternoon.

3. Grandmother had to pick from _____ all her grandchildren, the one who was to go home with her.

4. I can't decide _____ Math and Science.

5. The new doll was _____ the prettiest that I had ever seen.

6. It is easy for an astronomer to pick out Venus from
_____ the many stars.

7. It was dangerous to watch how the two animals
fought _____ themselves for their prey.

8. The spacecraft had to land _____
the two rocks.

9. Only the older children were _____ the
ones chosen to go to the rock festival.

Listen and check your answers.

Write sentences using among and between.

1. _____

_____

2. _____

_____

3. _____

_____

Good is an adjective. Use it to describe a noun (a person, a place, or a thing):

    That is a good painting. It's very dramatic.

    The weather has been very good recently. We've had lots of sunshine.

Well is an adverb. Use it to describe an action:

    She ran very well in the race. She won second prize.

    Miss Jones sings so well. She has a lovely voice.

Complete each sentence with good or well.

1. If you work _____, you will get good grades.

2. How _____ do you know that teacher?

3. You are such a _____ helper.

4. She is such a _____ student that all her friends want to study with her.

5. I like to go to a _____ restaurant on my birthday.

6. How _____ do you swim?

7. That was a _____ puppet show.

8. The circus dogs did a very _____ act.

9. The policeman did a very _____ job at finding the thief.

10. He played very _____ today.

Listen and check your answers.

Write sentences using well and good.

1. _____

2. _____

3. _____

4. _____

5. _____

Read the grammar rules.

	Subject Pronouns	Object Pronouns	Reflexive Pronouns
Singular	I	me	myself
	you	you	yourself
	he	him	himself
	she	her	herself
	it	it	itself
Plural	we	us	ourselves
	you	you	yourselves
	they	them	themselves

Use reflexive pronouns to refer back to the subject of the sentences:

    I wash myself.

    You've cut yourself.

    He taught himself how to use the computer.

    The children dress themselves in the morning.

Use reflexive pronouns to give emphasis to the person or thing that performs an action:

    Susie will prepare the lunch herself.

    I can do it myself.

Complete each sentence using an appropriate reflexive pronoun.

Example: Mary hurt herself when she fell off the swings.

1. The baby likes to look at _____ in the mirror.

2. The little girl dresses _____ every morning.

3. The policeman ran after the thief _____.

4. The teacher likes the students to correct their papers _____.

5. The principal said he would help raise the money for the new building _____.

6. The girls _____ decided to tell their parents the truth.

7. The nurse helped the sick woman to dress _____.

Write sentences using the given reflexive pronouns.

1. (myself) _____

_____

2. (ourselves) _____

_____

3. (himself) _____

_____

Use who to refer to a subject:
   Who planted the flowers this year?
Use whom to refer to an object after prepositions such as to, with, for, or from.
   With whom am I speaking?

Complete each sentence with who or whom.

1. From _____ did you get that money?

2. _____ brought this invitation?

3. I have always admired Dr. Thomas with _____ I studied for many years.

4. _____ discovered America?

5. _____ wants to go to the movies with me?

6. With _____ am I going to go home?

7. For _____ is this present?

8. _____ knows how far we have to go?

9. To _____ does this book belong?

10. _____ told you she is my sister?

11. With _____ are you going to the dance?

12. _____ is our new teacher?

Listen and check your answers.

Complete each question with who or whom.

Example: To whom are you writing a letter?

Dear Kyra,
xxoo

1. _____ knows the weather forecast for tomorrow?

2. With _____ are you traveling to France?

3. _____ is your handsome friend?

4. _____ sent that package to me?

5. For _____ is this sweater?

6. The students with _____ we spoke are over there.

7. _____ told you about this camp?

8. _____ wants to go to Alice's party?

9. _____ did you say has visited Egypt?

10. With _____ are you talking?

11. _____ is that person walking with Pat?

12. For _____ is this invitation?

Listen and check your answers.

Write two questions using who and
two questions using whom.

1. _____

2. _____

3. _____

4. _____

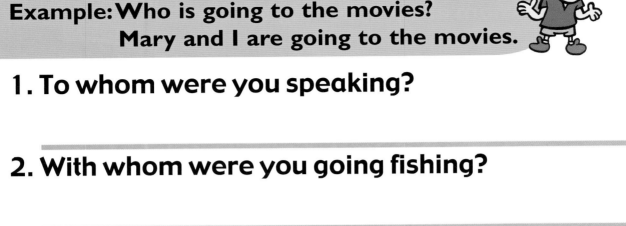

Answer each question.

Example: Who is going to the movies?
Mary and I are going to the movies.

1. To whom were you speaking?

_____

2. With whom were you going fishing?

_____

3. Who is that man?

_____

4. For whom is this present?

_____

Write a question with who and a question with whom and answer them.

1. _____

_____

2. _____

_____

A. Complete each sentence with between or among.

1. The oranges were divided _____ the children.

2. Some planets are difficult to see _____ all the stars.

3. He kicked the ball _____ the two trees.

4. Children, please don't fight _____ yourselves!

5. I can't decide _____ vanilla and chocolate.

6. He was lost _____ a crowd of strange people.

B. Complete each sentence with good or well.

1. How _____ do you know Thomas?

2. I bought a really _____ pair of shoes on Saturday.

3. The actors played their parts extremely _____.

4. It was a very _____ movie. I enjoyed it a lot.

5. The choir sang the song very _____.

6. He's a very _____ guard dog.

7. Oh dear! I didn't hit that one very _____.

8. Have a _____ time at the beach!

C. Complete each sentence using an appropriate reflexive pronoun.

1. She's only three years old but she can dress _____.

2. He's always looking at _____ in the mirror.

3. They _____ were the ones who stole the money!

4. Look! You've cut _____!

5. The cat can open the door _____.

6. I think we should do the work _____.

7. The food is ready. Now, all of you just help _____.

D. Write sentences using the given reflexive pronouns.

1. (yourself) _____

2. (ourselves) _____

3. (herself) _____

4. (myself) _____

E. Complete each question with who or whom.

1. From _____ is the letter?

2. _____ gave you a ride home?

3. For _____ is this present?

4. To _____ do these shoes belong?

5. _____ is the new Math teacher?

F. Look for information and write a report about Pasteur.

In France, nearly 100 years ago, a woman took her young son to Louis Pasteur's laboratory. The boy had been bitten by a mad dog with rabies.

Pasteur was a scientist who had developed a vaccine that could prevent rabies, but the vaccine had never been tried on human beings. The boy would die if he didn't get the vaccine.

What do you think happened? Why is Louis Pasteur considered one of the greatest scientists of all time?

Read about stories.

Three important elements in a story are the characters, the setting, and the plot.
The characters are the people or animals in a story. In many stories there are heroes, heroines, and villains. The author tells us how they look, how they feel, how they act, and what they say.
The setting is the place and the time in which a story takes place. A story may be set in the past, in the present, or in the future; in a far away country or even in an imaginary one.
The plot is the sequence of events of a story. Most stories have a beginning, a middle, and an ending. Often, a problem is introduced at the beginning of the story. Action and excitement build up as the story continues. At the end of the story we see how the problem was solved.

After each phrase, write if it refers to the characters, the setting, or the plot.

1. It was a beautiful place full of log cabins. _____

2. Richard was a strong, attractive man whose hobby was being a detective. _____

3. The woman had disappeared into the night. _____

4. The safe was open and the diamond was gone. _____

5. James Bond jumped from the plane. _____

6. The room was empty, dark, and unfriendly. _____

Read a story, or think of a well-known one like *Snow White,* and answer the questions.

1. Who is the main character in the story?

_____

_____

2. What is the setting of the story?

_____

_____

3. What problem does the main character have?

_____

_____

4. What is the most important event in the story?

_____

_____

5. How does the story end?

_____

_____

_____

_____

Read the information about book reports.

A book report tells us briefly what a book is about and provides a personal opinion about the book.
A book report should include:
- the title of the book
- the name of the author of the book and a few biographical facts such as when he/she was born, his/her nationality, other books he/she has written, etc.
- the main characters in the story, the setting, and the basic plot
- your personal opinion summarized into a few sentences

Title   **After the Fifth Grade... The World**
Author   **Claudia Mills**
Setting   **The story takes place mostly in one classroom in a school and in the homes of the two girls.**
Character(s)   **Heidi Ahlenslager**
     Lynette Lambert
     Mrs. Richardson

Plot

Two girls, Heidi and Lynette, are starting fifth grade and they have a horrible new teacher. Mrs. Richardson is mean and sarcastic and she insists that her students use one particular type of pen and white paper for everything they write as a way of learning discipline and responsibility. The two girls and their classmates try several times to win her over until finally they decide to write a newspaper article. Then, Mrs. Richardson becomes a loving teacher.

Opinion

I liked the story very much. It made me think how horrible it must be to have a teacher like that. It made me think how difficult it must be to change after so many years of doing the same thing. The book has many funny parts which I liked.

Answer the questions about the sample book report on the previous page.

1. What was the title of the book?

2. What is the author's name?

3. Who are the main characters in the book?

4. What is the setting of the story?

5. Does the report make you want to read the book? Why?

6. What is the writer's opinion of the book?

7. Have you ever met a teacher like Mrs. Richardson?

8. What do you think you would do if you had a teacher like Mrs. Richardson?

An outline organizes and summarizes information in a text into notes which include main ideas and supporting ideas.
Each main idea becomes a main topic and each supporting idea becomes a subtopic.
Main topics are listed in logical order. The subtopics are then grouped under the corresponding main topics.

Study the example of an outline.

Caterpillar to Butterfly

I. Egg
  - A. Laid by the butterfly
  - B. Laid on the inside of a leaf

II. Caterpillar

  - A. Grows from the egg
  - B. Spins a tiny silk thread around itself
  - C. Ties itself to the stem
  - D. Turns into a brown shell

III. Butterfly

  - A. Bursts from the brown shell in warm weather
  - B. Pulls itself out as a butterfly
  - C. Grows strong after a few hours
  - D. Flies away into the air

In your notebook, write an outline for a text.

An **informal letter** should be written with interesting, well-organized paragraphs that do not jump around from topic to topic. The letter should include specific details and information that the person who is receiving it will want to read about. A letter has five main parts:

Heading

This is where you write your address and today's date. Remember to put a comma between the city and the state. Put the **ZIP** code (postal code) after the state. Write the date on a separate line, with a comma between the day and the year. Line up the heading at the right of the page.

Greeting

This is the phrase with which you begin a letter. We normally write **Dear** and the name of the person we are writing to. Leave a space between the heading and the greeting. Place the greeting at the left margin and put a comma after it.

Body

This is the name we use for the main part of the letter. Remember to indent the first line of the letter and each new paragraph. Other lines should line up evenly at the left.

Closing

The closing is used to end the letter. Indent the closing, capitalize only the first word, and put a comma at the end. For someone you do not know very well, the most usual closing is **Yours sincerely**. With close friends, we use closings such as **With love**, **Yours**, or **Your friend**.

Signature

Sign using only your first name if you know the person well. Sign using your first and last names when writing to someone you do not know well. Line up your signature below the closing.

238 West 28 St,
New York, New York 10001   Heading

November 15, 2001

Dear Susan,   Greeting

    I'm so glad you are coming to visit us for
the Easter holidays. It's been so long since I saw
you that I'm not sure I'll recognize you. The last
time we spent a holiday together we were both   Body
five years old. Do you remember? I still love
going to the beach, swimming, and even making
sand castles! How about you?

    We're all looking forward to seeing you
soon. Write when you know the exact date that
you are arriving.

    Your friend,   Closing

    Anna   Signature

Addressing Envelopes

The return address (your name and address) should be written in the upper left-hand corner of the front of the envelope.

Write the address of the person to whom you are writing in the center. Use a title (Mr., Miss, Mrs., Dr., etc.) here but not in the return address. See that addresses in English-speaking countries are written in a different way.

Anna Smith
238 West 28 St.
New York, New York 10001

Miss Susan Miner
301 America Road
Eagle Pass, Texas 46002

Address the envelope with your address and the address of a friend in another city.

We write business letters to an organization or a company to place orders for goods, to request information, to make a complaint, etc. Unlike informal or personal letters which are written by hand, business letters are always typed on a typewriter or a computer. A business letter has six main parts:

Heading

This is where you write your address and today's date. Remember to put a comma between the city and the state. Put the ZIP code (postal code) after the state. Write the date on a separate line, with a comma between the date and the year. Line up the heading at the right of the page.

Inside address

This is the complete name and address of the person or organization (or both) that you are writing to. Write the inside address at the left-hand margin.

Greeting

This is the phrase with which you begin a letter. We normally write Dear and the title and name of the person we are writing to. When you don't know the name of the person, write Dear Sir or Madam. Leave a space between the heading and the greeting. Place the greeting at the left margin and put a comma after it.

Body

This is the name we use for the main part of the letter. Remember to indent the first line of the letter and each new paragraph. Other lines should line up evenly at the left.

Closing

The closing is used to end the letter. Indent the closing, capitalize only the first word, and put a comma at the end. In a business letter, the most usual closing is Yours sincerely.

Signature

In a business letter, sign using both your first and last name. Write your signature clearly. Type your name below your handwritten signature. Line up your signature below the closing.

Write the names of the six parts of the letter in the correct spaces.

2194 West Avenue
San Antonio, Texas 16325

_____

November 29, 2001

Nintendo Corp.
413 North Avenue
San Antonio, Texas 16409

_____

Dear Sir,

_____

I am interested in buying your products for my office. Please send me your latest catalogs and price lists. I look forward to hearing from you.

Yours sincerely,

Carol Webster

_____

Dr. Carol Webster

_____

Useful tips

Be brief

Business people do not have time for letters which take a long time to state their purpose.

Be clear and complete

Give all the necessary information and arrange it so that it will be easy to follow. Be clear about what you want. For example, state clearly if you are placing an order or asking for information.

Be neat

Business letters should be typed, not handwritten. Remember to be careful with the presentation of your letter and the impression that it will have on the reader when he/she receives it.

Write a letter to either
    a) a bookstore asking for a specific book on a subject
    that interests you, or
    b) a camping store asking for camping equipment
    catalogs. Address the envelope.

A. After each phrase, write if it refers to characters, setting, or plot. For each answer, give a reason.

Example: A dark, deserted castle...
Setting, because it tells us where the story takes place.

1. The queen was very old and very sad.

_____

2. He quickly jumped into his car and drove away.

_____

3. It was a small, dark room. The windows were dirty.

_____

4. As we approached the lake, we saw an amazing sight.

_____

5. Tom was the tallest kid in the class. We all called him...

_____

B. Punctuate each item correctly.

1. Your friend

2. Dear Sir

3. 3112 Riverside Ave

4. December 22 2001

5. With lots of love

6. July 14 2001

7. Yours sincerely

8. Dear Mr. Smith

9. 495 Ocean Boulevard

10. October 23 2000

C. Label the business letter with the correct terms from the box.

Inside address   Greeting   Heading
Closing   Signature   Body

368 Pike's Lane
San Diego, Cal. 34008

1. _____

May 17, 2001

2. _____

Southern School Supplies
5884 Trent Road
San Diego, Cal. 35991

Dear Sir,

3. _____

   I would like to order the following school supplies from your 2002 catalog:

4. _____

25 boxes of pencils (No. 16)	$ 52.50
4 chalkboards (Model 32)	115.30
1 overhead projector	360.00
	$ 527.80

   I enclose a money order for the total amount plus a shipping fee of $18.50.
   I look forward to receiving my supplies.

Yours sincerely,

5. _____

Jane Hughes

6. _____

Jane Hughes

D. Write an informal letter **to a friend who has moved to another town. Address the envelope.**

_____

_____

_____

_____

_____

_____

_____

_____

_____

_____

_____

_____

_____

_____

_____

_____

_____

A. Correct each sentence with capital letters, periods, question marks, exclamation points, apostrophes, **and** commas **where necessary.**

1. my mother went to andrews hospital to see my aunt

2. the baby was born on december 23 2001 in san antonio texas

3. Mary is going to go see dr green tomorrow

4. hooray hooray our basketball team won again

5. did she read sleeping beauty

B. Write the plural form **of each noun.**

1. deer _____   7. woman _____

2. ox _____   8. calf _____

3. man _____   9. mouse _____

4. child _____   10. tooth _____

5. trout _____   11. fly _____

6. thief _____   12. dress _____

C. Write the abbreviated form **of each noun.**

1. Sunday _____   6. Doctor _____

2. Friday _____   7. Company _____

3. February _____   8. Kilometer _____

4. December _____   9. Meters _____

5. Saturday _____   10. Street _____

D. Write the plural of each noun.

1. fox _____
2. church _____
3. dish _____
4. peach _____
5. foot _____
6. class _____
7. bunch _____
8. plant _____
9. goose _____
10. pony _____

11. butterfly _____
12. wolf _____
13. knife _____
14. leaf _____
15. fish _____
16. box _____
17. lady _____
18. baby _____
19. house _____
20. army _____

E. In each sentence, underline the correct pronoun.

1. We/Us went to the movies on Saturday.

2. My mother took we/us shopping.

3. She/Her is a famous actress.

4. Robert took he/him to school this morning.

5. He sent her/she flowers for her birthday.

6. He put them/they in his desk for safekeeping.

7. Mark and I/me are taking piano lessons.

8. I wrote them/they a letter a month ago.

F. After each sentence, write if the verb to be is a linking verb or a helping verb.

1. This is yesterday's newspaper.
2. I am wearing a new hat. _____
3. You are my best friend. _____
4. Mary is singing in the choir. _____
5. They are going to a summer camp. _____
6. The children are eating hot dogs. _____
7. The dog is barking at the children. _____
8. The dinosaur is huge. _____

G. In each question, underline the correct form of the verb. Then, answer each question with an affirmative or a negative answer.

Example: <u>Does</u>/Do she want some chocolate ice cream?
Yes, she does.

1. Does/Did the girls go to their swimming class?
   No, _____
2. Does/Do the students eat their lunch at 12:00?
   No, _____
3. Does/Did the actress receive an Oscar?
   Yes, _____
4. Does/Do the teacher grade the homework?
   Yes, _____
5. Does/Did the dogs chase the cats?
   No, _____
6. Does/Did the mothers help the children?
   Yes, _____

H. Read the information about owls and write an outline.

Owls

Owls are interesting birds. They sleep in the daytime and hunt for food at night.

Some farmers like owls because they catch mice and rats for food. Owls also eat worms, grasshoppers, and other insects. An owl swallows its food whole. Later, it spits up the bones, skin, and hair in little balls.

Owls gather grass and feathers to build their nests in hollow tree trunks. Owls may lay four or five eggs.

There are many kinds of owls and they come in different sizes and colors. We find white owls in the far north of the United States and common brown owls and elf owls in Texas.

Owls lose their homes when forests are cut down. Some people are now working to pass laws to protect these distinctive birds.

A. Write sentences that show possession.

1. toys/children

_____

2. hat/grandmother

_____

3. dresses/women

_____

B. In each sentence, circle the subject and underline the predicate.

1. These waiters and waitresses get very good tips.
2. Elephants are very interesting animals to write about.
3. Mobile homes and trailers are very popular in the United States.
4. Seals like to swim near rocks.

C. In each sentence, circle the adjectives and underline the nouns that they describe.

1. The handsome man looked silently at the attractive woman.
2. The colorful flowers looked nice in the cheerful kitchen.
3. The beautiful butterflies were flying near the flower pots.

D. Write sentences with the given adverbs.

1. (slowly) _____

_____

2. (inside) _____

_____

3. (tomorrow) _____

_____

E. Rewrite each sentence with the correct subject pronoun.

1. Mark and Robert are going to a summer camp.

_____

2. My teacher lost her purse yesterday.

_____

3. The picture is very beautiful.

_____

F. Write sentences with the given words.

1. (good) _____

2. (better) _____

3. (best) _____

4. (bad) _____

5. (worse) _____

6. (worst) _____

G. Change each sentence to the past tense, and add a time reference (yesterday, last year, etc.).

1. She gives the baby her bottle every three hours.

_____

2. The plumber makes a mess when he fixes the sink.

_____

3. Henry writes a letter every Saturday.

_____

H. Complete the table with the correct form of each verb.

Present	Past	Past Participle
choose		
	went	
have		
		brought
	ran	
see		
	fed	
		taught
think		
buy		

I. Write a synonym for each word.

1. small _____
2. put _____
3. error _____
4. under _____

5. happy _____
6. begin _____
7. large _____
8. smart _____

J. Write a homophone for each word.

1. flower _____
2. sun _____
3. ant _____

4. weak _____
5. for _____
6. choose _____

K. Write an antonym **for each word.**

1. day _____   6. hot _____
2. tall _____   7. wet _____
3. present _____   8. young _____
4. open _____   9. begin _____
5. white _____   10. difficult _____

L. Write three sentences using compound words**.**

1. _____

_____

2. _____

_____

3. _____

_____

M. Write questions using the words in parentheses.

1. (she... going to... some cookies)

_____

2. (the architect... will build... new...)

_____

3. (students... going to... river)

_____

4. (the children... will have a good time... with the clowns)

_____

N. Look for information about ostriches (or some other species of birds) and write a report.

Where do these birds live? How big are they? What do they eat? Do they lay eggs? How many eggs do they lay at a time?

A. Write one sentence with some and one with any.

1. _____

_____

2. _____

_____

B. Write one sentence with something and one with anything.

1. _____

_____

2. _____

_____

C. Complete the table with the correct reflexive pronouns.

I		it	itself
you (singular)	yourself	we	
he		you (plural)	
she		they	

D. Write sentences using the given pronouns.

1. (who) _____

_____

2. (whom) _____

_____

151

E. Look for information about Saturn (or another planet) and write a report about it.